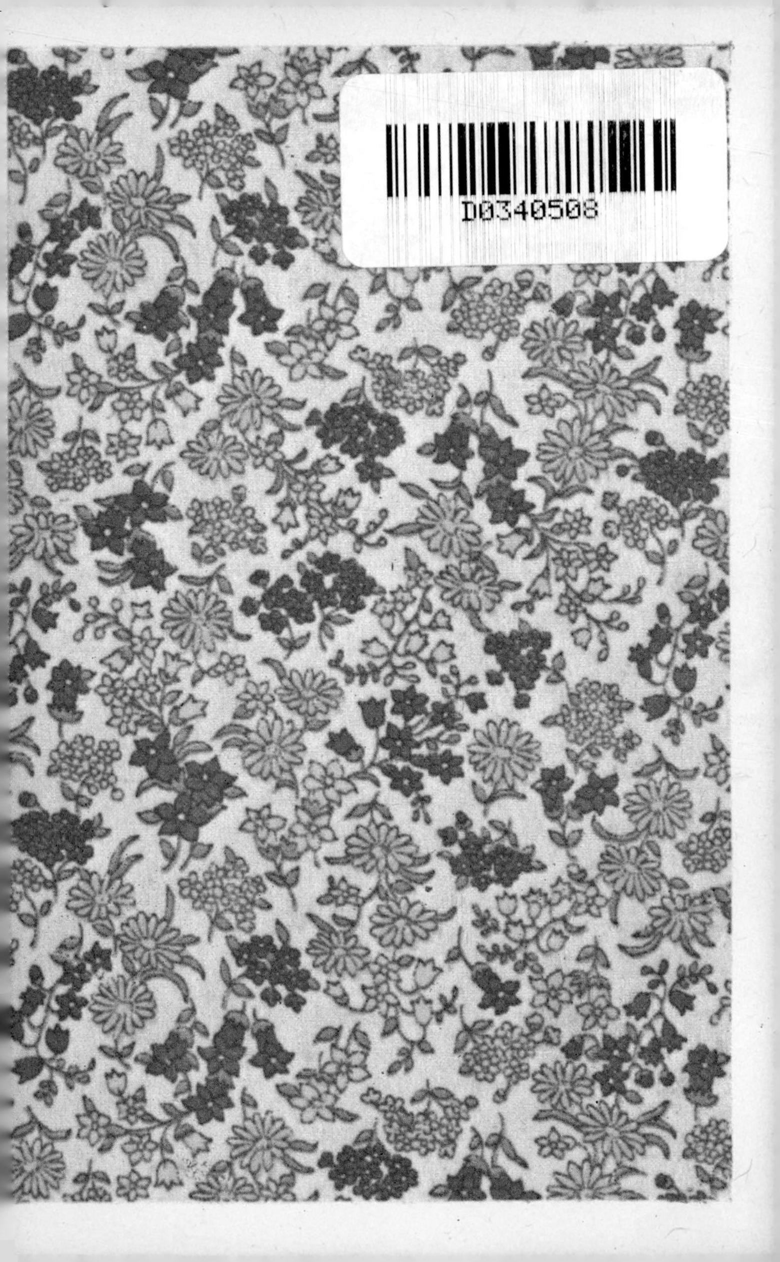

To Mother
with love
from
Jodi

MOTHER is another name for love

written by:
MYRA ZIRKLE

designed by:
ELANA KUCHARIK

illustrated by:
LINDA CROCKETT

A Mother is someone
who's happy when
you're happy...
and knows just how
you feel when you're
not.

You don't mind
telling her when
you're a little scared,
'cause you know she
won't laugh.

She works harder than
anyone else you know...
(and doesn't seem to
mind)
but she's always there
whenever you need
help.

She's always willing
to listen to <u>your</u>
side of the story...
And she doesn't often say
"I told you so"--even
when she told you so.

REPORT CARD

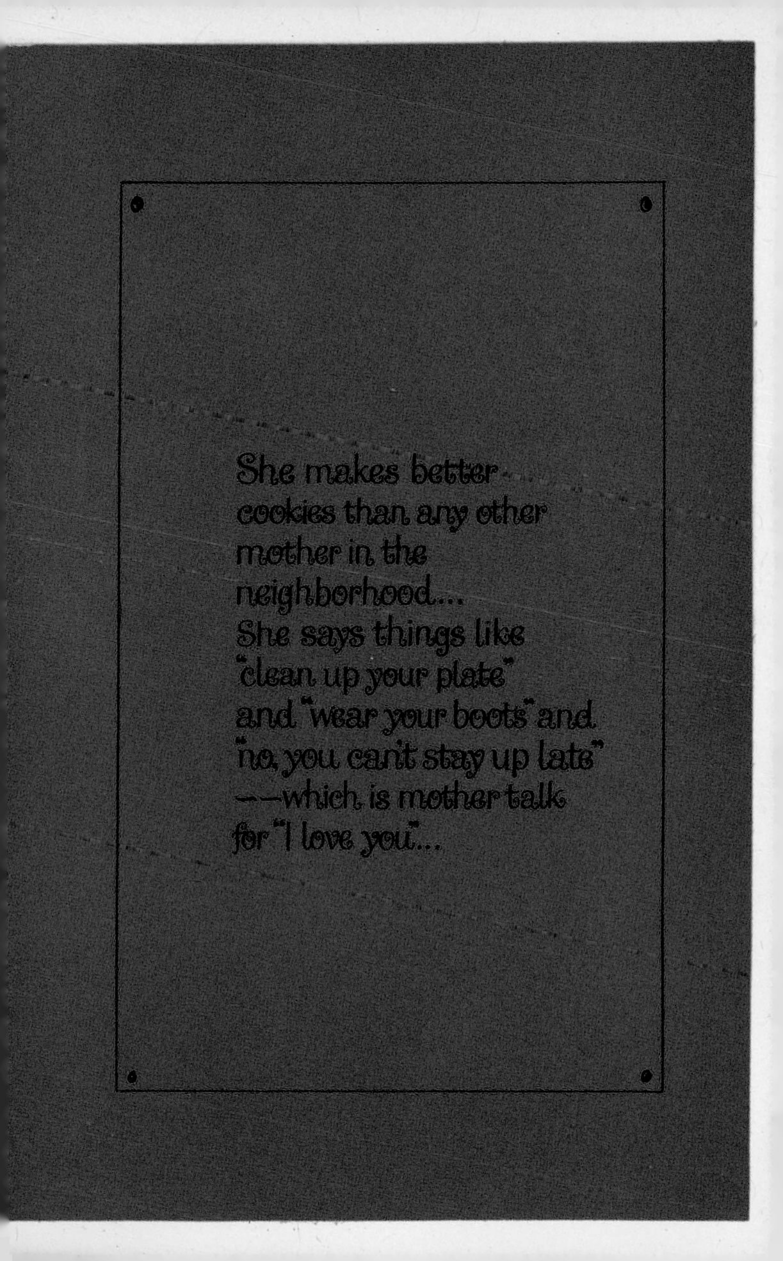

She makes better
cookies than any other
mother in the
neighborhood...
She says things like
"clean up your plate"
and "wear your boots" and
"no, you can't stay up late"
——which is mother talk
for "I love you"...

And she makes you do
things you'd rather not
because she knows
that later on, you'll
be glad...
and she does things
she'd rather not
for the same reason!

She loves getting you
things you've always
wanted...
(...even if something
<u>she's</u> always wanted
has to wait a little
while)

And she always has
the best medicine
for your little cuts
and bruises.
A mother does special
things for you that
no one else would
even think of...

She's proud of you
when you start doing
things on your own...
and she's never
surprised when you
do something well,
'cause she knew
all along you could!

A mother has all sorts of special skills...like keeping the house looking nice...

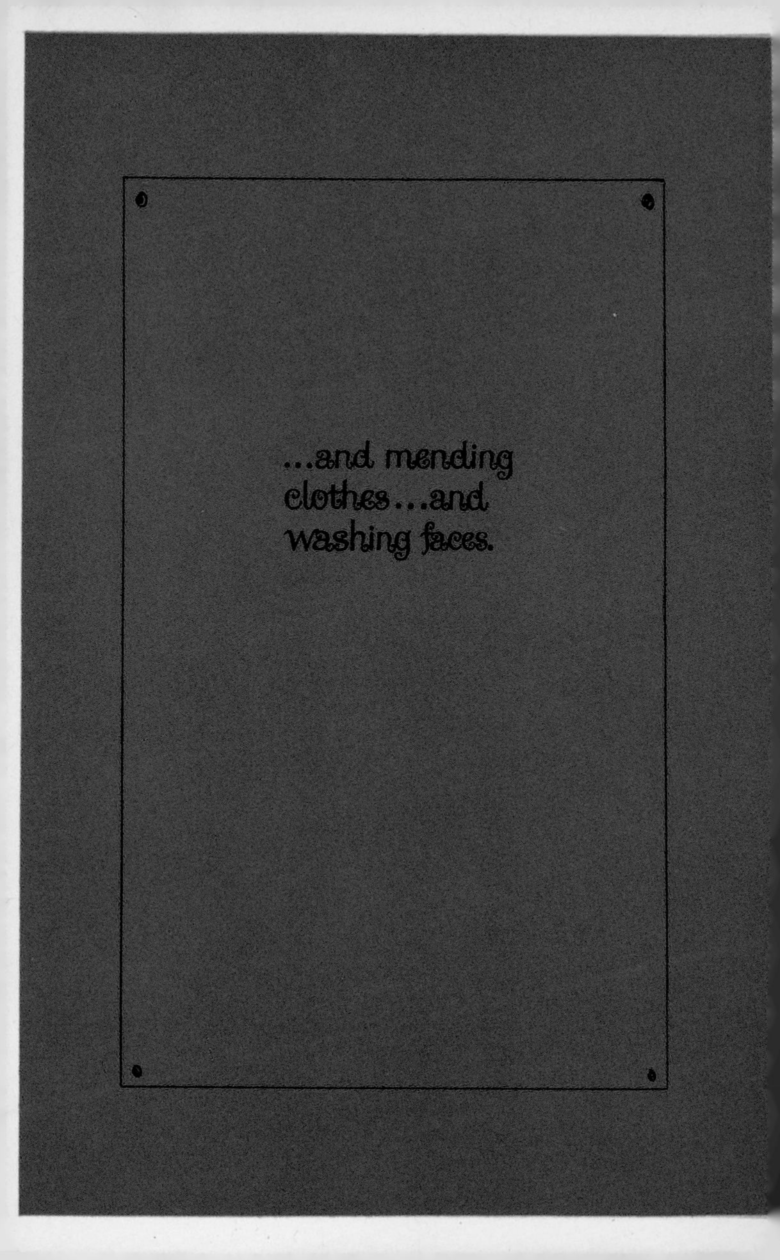
...and mending
clothes...and
washing faces.

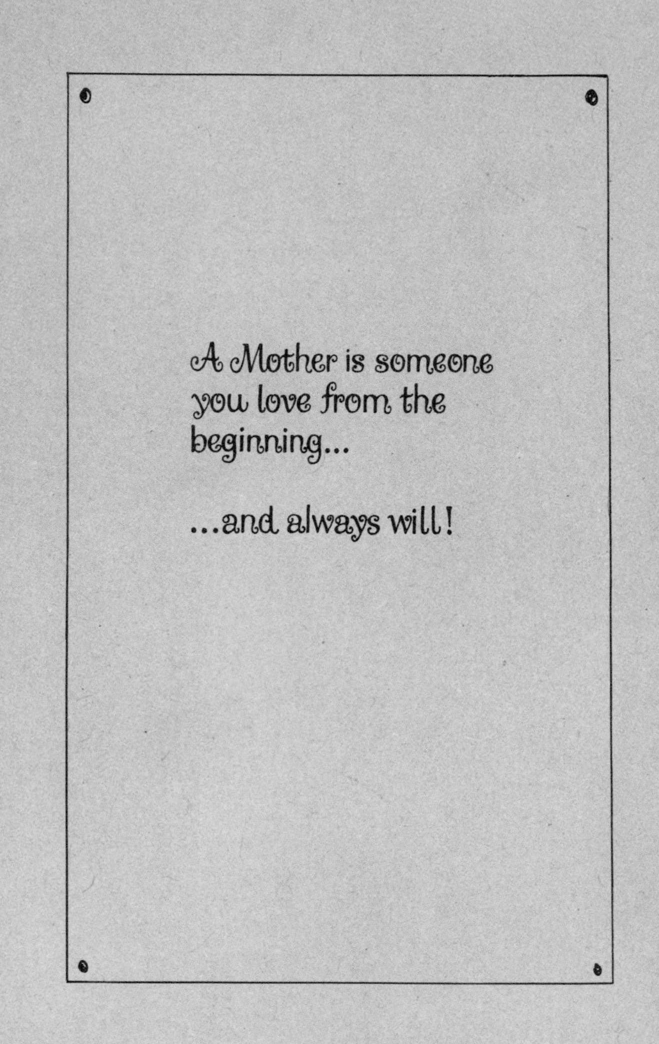

A Mother is someone
you love from the
beginning...

...and always will!

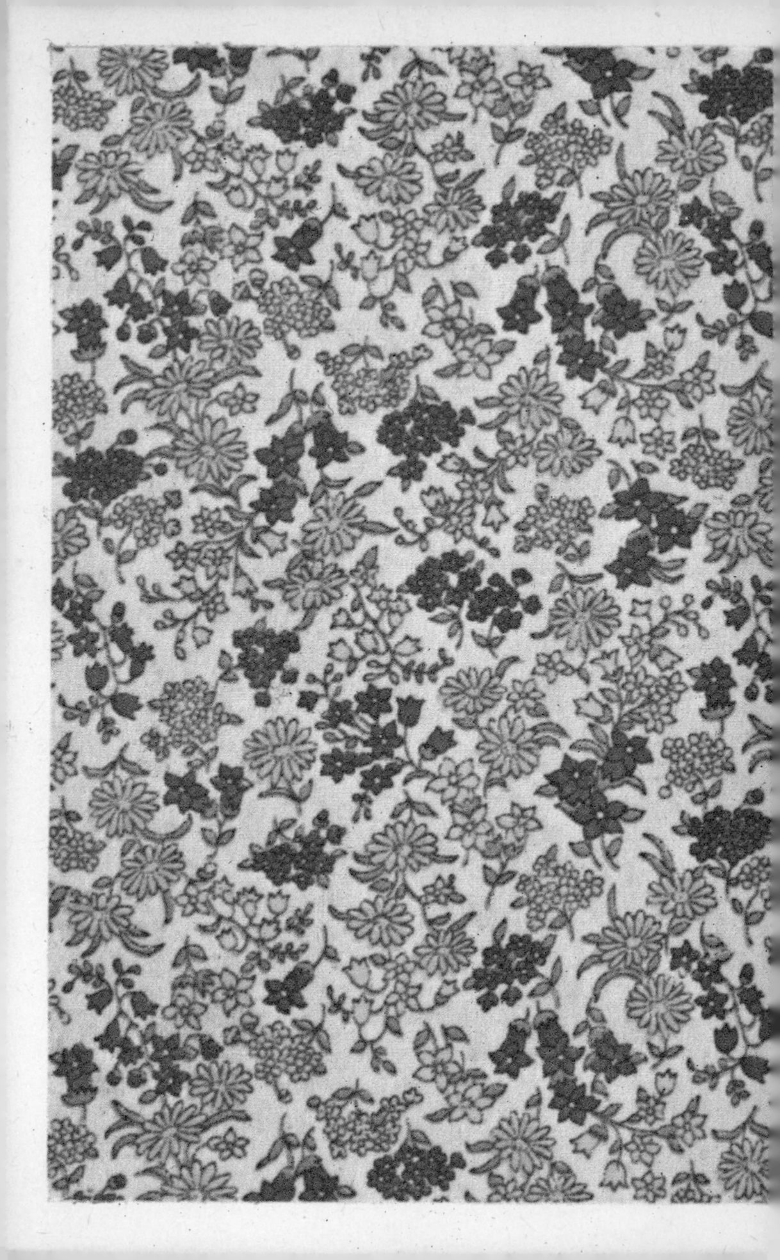